A Do-It-Yourself Yearbook

Creative Ideas for Making a Personalized Memory Book

Written by Pamela Amick Klawitter, Ed.D. & Linda Schwartz
Illustrated by Bev Armstrong ◆ Cover Art by Kathy Parks

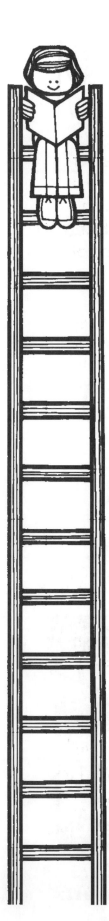

The
Learning
Works

Typesetting and Editorial Production:
Clark Editorial & Design

Copyright © 1999
The Learning Works, Inc.
Santa Barbara, California 93160

ISBN: 0-88160-239-6
LW 334

Printed in the United States of America.

Introduction

A Do-It-Yourself Yearbook is an exciting and motivating way for students to keep an ongoing journal about themselves throughout the school year. The book is divided into sections by months, with five exercises per month of the school year from which to choose. The activities may be completed independently or in a group setting. Students can make and illustrate folders to keep their pages in as they work. The young authors can then design original covers for their completed books at the end of the school year.

A Do-It-Yourself Yearbook provides opportunities for creative thinking, art, and creative writing as students gain a better understanding and insight into themselves. By doing several exercises a month, each student will have a meaningful memento at the end of the school year—a yearbook worth saving and reflecting upon, both now and in the future.

Following the monthly activity pages is a selection of expander pages including seasonal activities, story pages, and autograph pages. These may be added to the monthly activities to augment student books.

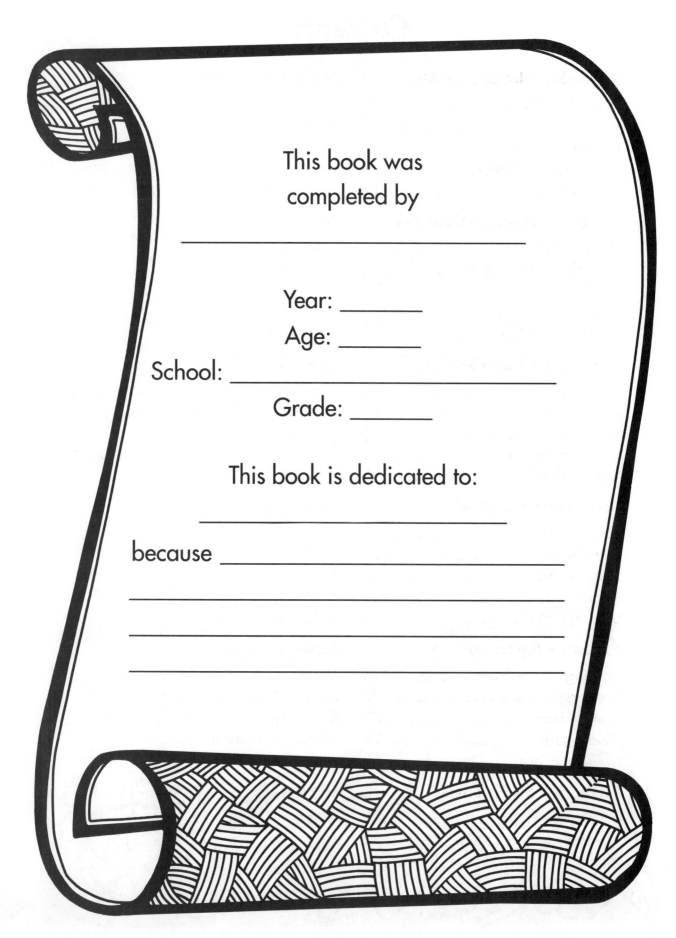

This book was
completed by

_____

Year: _____

Age: _____

School: _____

Grade: _____

This book is dedicated to:

_____

because _____

_____

_____

_____

Contents

Magnificent Me

My name is

_____

and I live in

_____
city

_____
state

I was born on

_____
month, day, year

in

_____
city, state

I live with _____

_____

_____

My home is:

_____

_____

_____

_____

_____

This is how I look:

_____

_____

_____

_____

_____

Here I Am!

I drew this picture of myself at the beginning of the school year.

My Handwriting

This is a sample of my best handwriting. I will save it and compare this page with my handwriting at the end of the school year.

Copy this paragraph:

This is a sample of my best handwriting. It is part of my own personal yearbook. Each month during this school year I will add a few more pages to my book. Keeping this record will help me remember what a great year I had. It will be interesting to look back through this book in the future and see what happened this year.

My Goals for the Year

Goals at Home

This year I would like to help out more at home by _____

_____

A new hobby I would like to try is _____

_____

I would like to try and become better at _____

because_____

Another goal of mine at home is _____

_____

Goals at School

I would like to do better in the area of _____

_____

I would like to become better friends with _____

_____

A study habit I would like to improve is _____

_____

Another goal of mine at school is_____

_____

A Do-It-Yourself Yearbook
© The Learning Works, Inc.

What If?

If I could be any person in the world, I would be _____

because_____

If I could be an animal, I would be _____

because_____

If I could live during any period in history, I would choose _____

_____ because _____

_____

If I could live in any city in the world, I would choose _____

because_____

If I could change one thing about myself, it would be _____

because_____

If I could have any talent I wanted, I would choose _____

because_____

If I had all the money I wanted, I would_____

because_____

If I could do one thing to make the world a better place, I would

_____

because_____

More About Me

A place that is very special to me

is _____ because _____

_____

_____

Some of my talents are

_____

_____

_____

I can often be found

_____

_____

_____

In my spare time I like to

_____

_____

_____

When I'm with my friends, I

_____

_____

_____

My Hobbies and Interests

I like to collect _____

_____

Sports and games I enjoy _____

_____

_____

I think it would be fun to learn more about:

_____

_____

_____

Things I enjoy doing when I have time to spend as I please

at home: _____

at school: _____

with my friends: _____

with my family: _____

by myself: _____

I take lessons in: _____

I belong to these groups and clubs: _____

_____

_____

My Travels

The best trip I ever took was to _____

While I was there, I _____

_____

_____

I have visited the following places:

☐ airport   ☐ beach   ☐ national park

☐ amusement park   ☐ circus   ☐ observatory

☐ art gallery   ☐ factory   ☐ planetarium

☐ ballpark   ☐ museum   ☐ zoo

☐ other _____

I have visited these states: _____

_____

I have visited these foreign countries: _____

_____

I would like to visit these three places: _____

_____

_____

My Top Ten

These are ten things I could never do without.

I'd Like You to Meet

I would like to introduce you

to _____

because _____

_____

_____

_____

_____

_____

_____

_____

_____

_____

_____

_____

_____

I Wish

These are the things
I'd wish for
if I had three wishes:

_____

_____

_____

_____

_____

_____

In My Opinion

These are my feelings on the subjects of:

tolerance

drugs

curfews

the Internet

FOR FUN Sound off on a topic of your choice. Make a poster that shows your opinion on something that is important to you.

My Feelings

Three things that really make me *mad* are _____

_____

One of the *saddest* days I can remember is _____

_____

One of the *silliest* things that ever happened to me was

_____

Once I was very *frightened* when _____

_____

I felt very *lonely* when _____

_____

I was really *excited* when _____

_____

When I feel *nervous*, I always _____

_____

What Do You See?

Everyone sees me in a different way. These are three adjectives each of these people would use to describe me.

My mom thinks I'm:

_____

_____

_____

My dad thinks I'm

_____

_____

_____

I think I'm

_____

_____

_____

My teacher thinks I'm

_____

_____

_____

My friend _____ thinks I'm

_____

_____

_____

My friend _____ thinks I'm

_____

_____

_____

- ☐ artistic
- ☐ athletic
- ☐ brave
- ☐ careful
- ☐ clever
- ☐ creative
- ☐ curious
- ☐ dependable
- ☐ easygoing

- ☐ energetic
- ☐ friendly
- ☐ fun-loving
- ☐ funny
- ☐ generous
- ☐ gullible
- ☐ hard-working
- ☐ honest
- ☐ independent

- ☐ kind
- ☐ loving
- ☐ messy
- ☐ musical
- ☐ organized
- ☐ ornery
- ☐ outgoing
- ☐ polite
- ☐ quiet

- ☐ respectful
- ☐ serious
- ☐ smart
- ☐ stubborn
- ☐ talkative
- ☐ thoughtful
- ☐ trusting
- ☐ weird
- ☐ _____

Guess What!

Here are three fabulous things I bet you didn't know about me!

School Daze

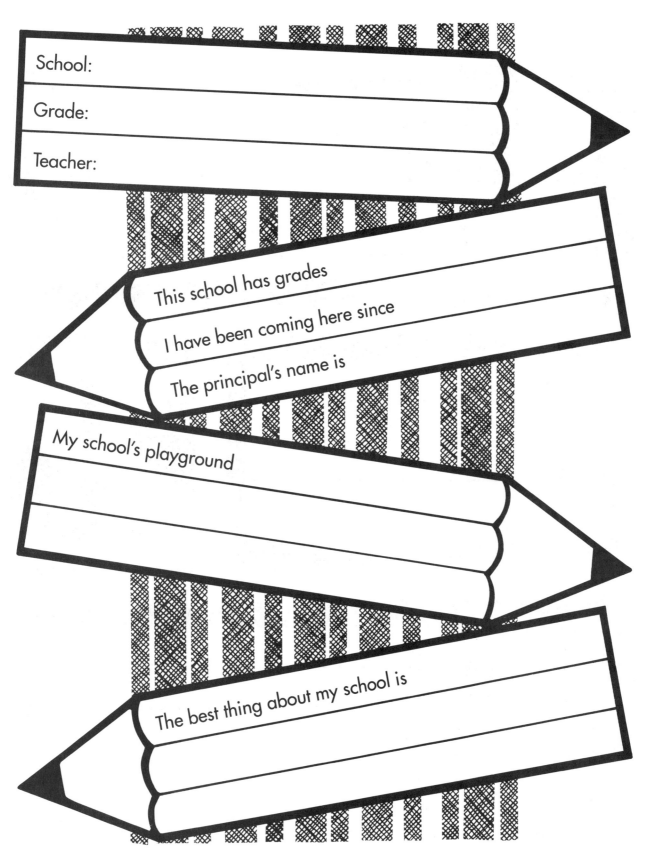

School:

Grade:

Teacher:

This school has grades

I have been coming here since

The principal's name is

My school's playground

The best thing about my school is

Class Act

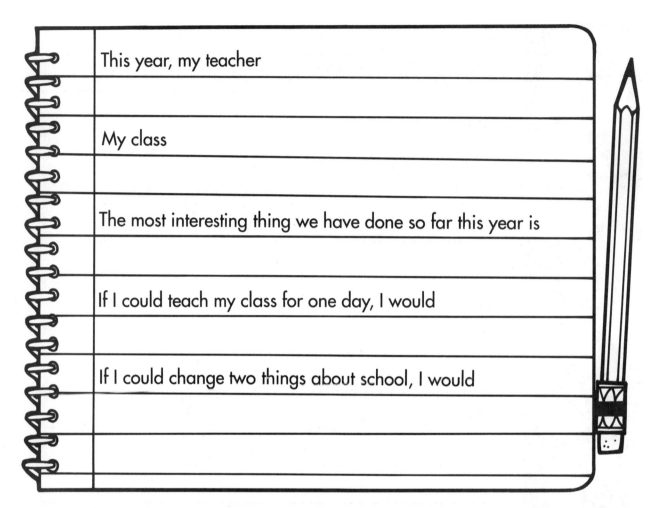

This year, my teacher

My class

The most interesting thing we have done so far this year is

If I could teach my class for one day, I would

If I could change two things about school, I would

The best thing about school this year is

The worst thing about school this year is

A Day at School

Before school, I_____

_____

I get to school by _____

In the morning, my class _____

_____

_____

_____

At lunch time, _____

_____

_____

After lunch, my class _____

_____

_____

_____

At the end of the school day, _____

_____

_____

After school, I_____

_____

_____

_____

My Teacher

My teacher's name is _____ .

My teacher was born in _____ , _____ .
                                          city   state

Other jobs held:

Hobbies and interests:

The best thing about my teacher:

What my teacher likes most about teaching:

My teacher's favorites

color:

sport:

movie:

food:

kind of book:

kind of music:

vacation spot:

season:

Exciting E-Mail

These are the two top news stories
from my classroom so far this year.

Hot Dog! We're Friends!

I am happy when a friend _____

_____

I am unhappy when a friend _____

I think it is important for a friend to be _____

because_____

I enjoy talking to my friends about _____

_____

One nice thing I have done for a friend is_____

_____

One nice thing a friend has done for me is_____

_____

Some of my friends are _____

_____

FOR FUN Write a story about a special time you shared with a friend.

Speaking of Friends

The best time I ever had with a friend was

The worst disagreement I ever had with a friend was

I think it is important for a friend to be:

- ☐ athletic
- ☐ cheerful
- ☐ creative
- ☐ fair
- ☐ forgiving
- ☐ helpful
- ☐ kind
- ☐ polite
- ☐ smart
- ☐ trustworthy
- ☐ truthful
- ☐ understanding

Some things I enjoy doing with my friends are:

I am a great friend because I

Friendly Faces

Here are some pictures of my friends.

A Do-It-Yourself Yearbook
© The Learning Works, Inc.

Glad to Help

I'm a helpful member of my family because

I help the environment by

If I could spend $100 to help someone else, I would

I will never forget the time

helped me by

My Ideal Friend

If I could put together the ideal friend, I would choose characteristics from all of my friends. I would include:

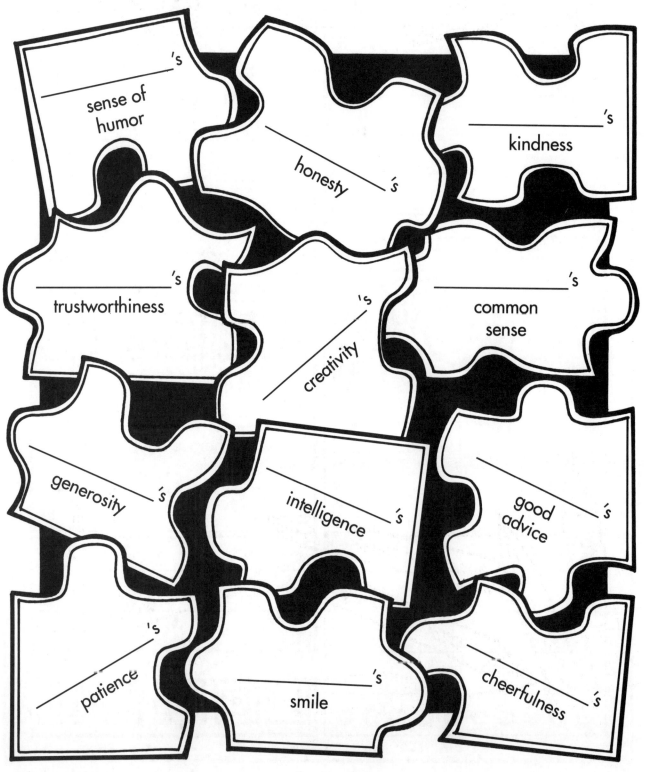

_____'s sense of humor

_____'s honesty

_____'s kindness

_____'s trustworthiness

_____'s creativity

_____'s common sense

_____'s generosity

_____'s intelligence

_____'s good advice

_____'s patience

_____'s smile

_____'s cheerfulness

My Favorite Place

Here is a picture of my very favorite
place in the whole world!

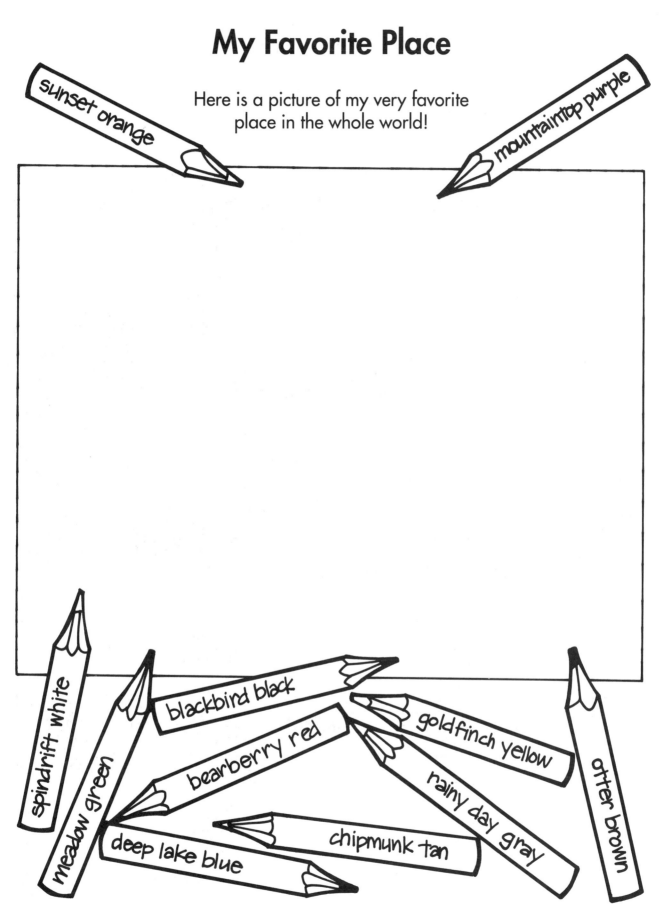

All-Time Favorites

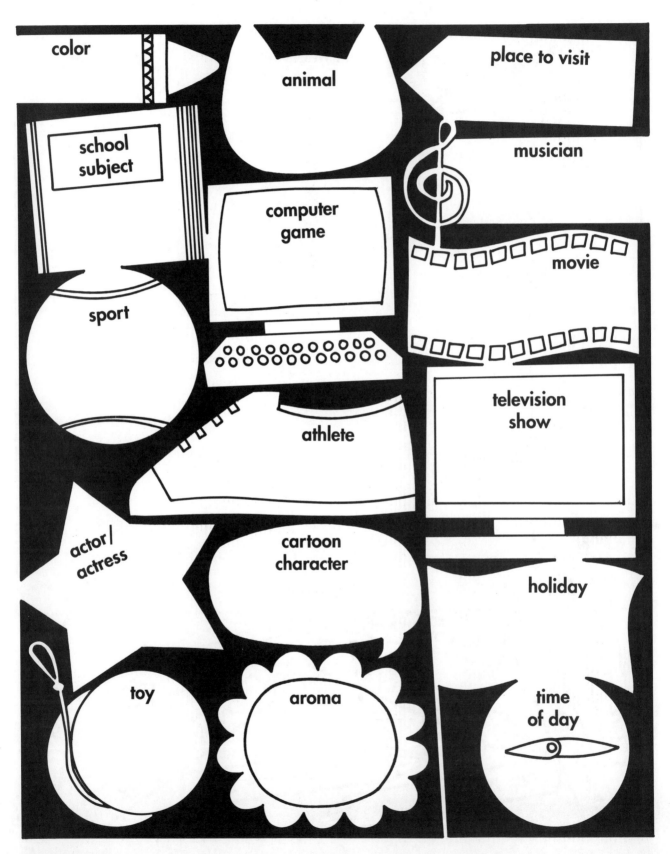

color

animal

place to visit

school subject

musician

computer game

movie

sport

athlete

television show

actor/actress

cartoon character

holiday

toy

aroma

time of day

Just for Fun

These are pictures of my favorite pastimes.

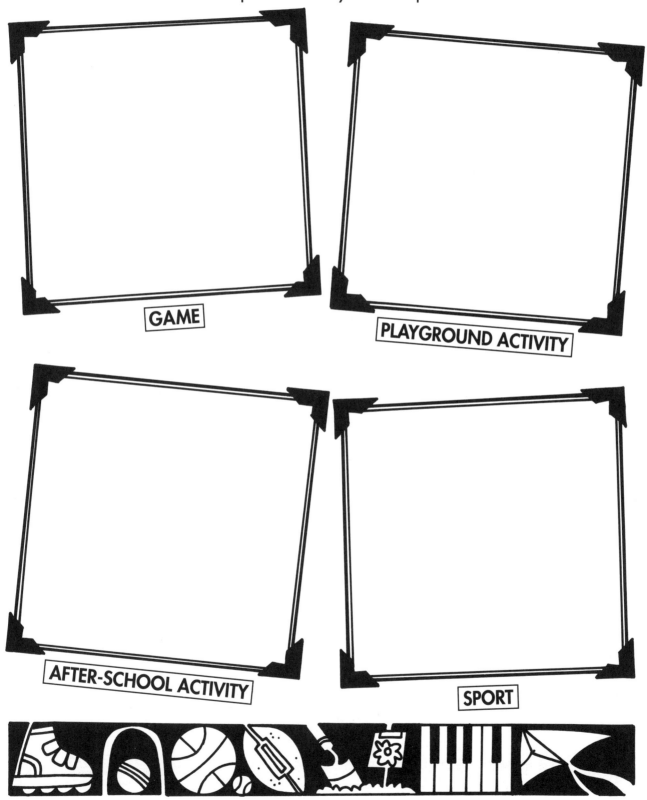

GAME

PLAYGROUND ACTIVITY

AFTER-SCHOOL ACTIVITY

SPORT

Favorite Books

The kinds of books I like to read are _____
_____

My favorite place to read is _____
_____

Some of the books I own are _____
_____

The very best book I ever read was _____
_____ by _____

I liked that book because _____
_____

My favorite author is _____
because _____

Three books I plan to read soon are _____
_____

Greetings

Design a postcard that you might send from your favorite vacation spot. Draw and color a picture on the front and write an address and a message on the back.

front

back

School News

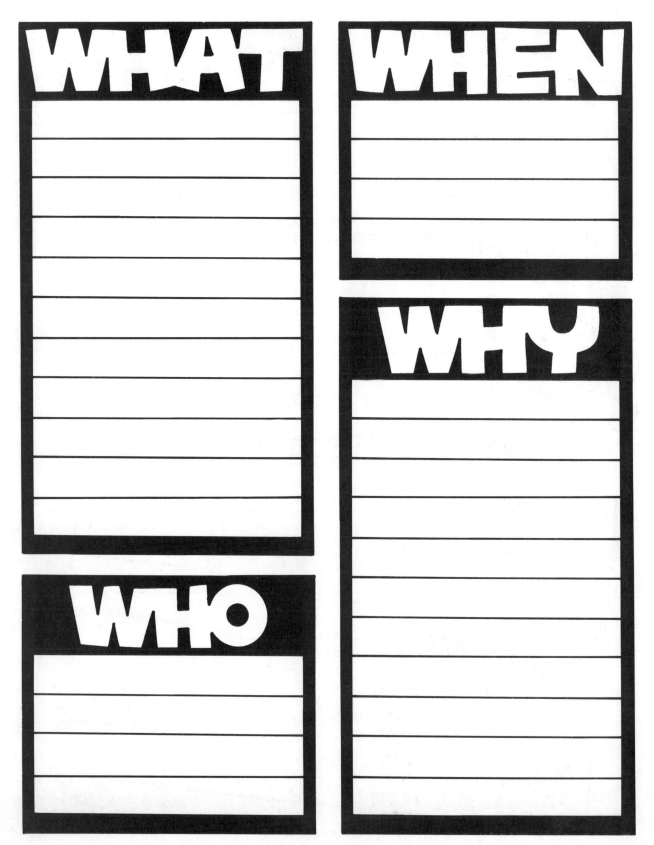

WHAT

WHEN

WHY

WHO

What's Hot?

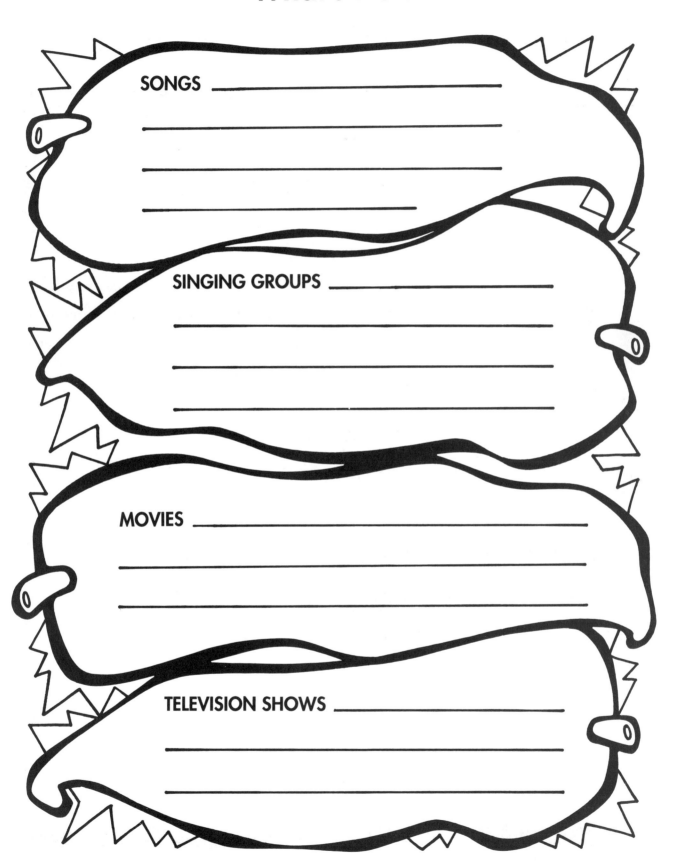

SONGS _____

_____

_____

SINGING GROUPS _____

_____

_____

MOVIES _____

_____

_____

TELEVISION SHOWS _____

_____

In the News

These are some of the stories that were in the news this month.

Front Page News

_____

_____

_____

_____

Weather

_____

_____

_____

_____

Sports

_____

_____

_____

_____

Fast Facts

Here are some facts to remember from this year. I recorded them on: _____

month, day, year

In Office

United States President:

_____

Vice President:

_____

Governor of my state:

_____

Mayor of my city:

_____

The Stock Market
(price per share)

Coca-Cola: _____

McDonald's: _____

Nike: _____

PepsiCo: _____

Other Favorite Companies:

Company	Price
_____	_____
_____	_____

PRICES

candy bar _____   pair of jeans _____

gallon of milk _____   haircut _____

school lunch _____   newspaper _____

movie ticket _____   postage stamp _____

loaf of bread _____   pay phone call _____

Who's In the News?

These people made headlines this year.

NEWS! NEWS!

Politics

Who? _____

Why? _____

_____

_____

_____

Science

Who? _____

Why? _____

_____

_____

_____

Sports

Who? _____

Why? _____

_____

_____

_____

Entertainment

Who? _____

Why? _____

_____

_____

_____

Field Trip Fun

WHERE WE WENT

WHAT WE DID

MY BEST MEMORY

Awesome Assembly

This is who came and what happened:

_____

_____

_____

_____

_____

_____

_____

_____

_____

_____

Playground Pranks

These are the two funniest things I've seen on the playground this year.

Fashion Fads

Here are this year's most popular fashion fads:

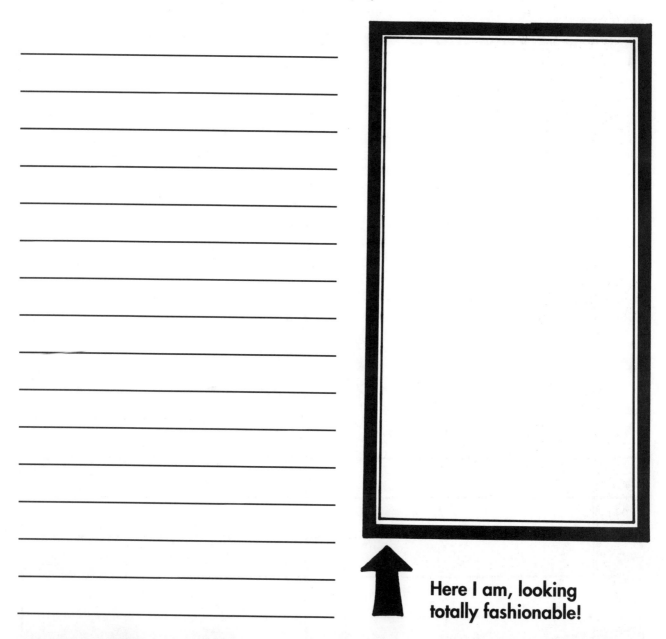

Here I am, looking totally fashionable!

Good Sports!

This is a great sporting event we had at school.

_____

_____

_____

_____

_____

_____

_____

Choosing a Career

In the future, I think I would like to work: Check all
that apply.

☐ indoors   ☐ outdoors   ☐ at night   ☐ during the day

☐ alone   ☐ with children   ☐ with adults

☐ at a desk   ☐ standing up   ☐ with machines   ☐ with animals

☐ wearing a uniform   ☐ in regular clothes

☐ in one place   ☐ traveling around

One job I am thinking about is _____

because _____

I will need the following education or training for this occupation: _____

_____

_____

An advantage of this job is

_____

_____

A disadvantage of this job is

_____

_____

Here is a picture of me
at the job I have chosen.

My Dreams

for myself

for my family

for the world

My Time Capsule

To help remember this year, these are the four most important things
I would put in my time capsule and the reason for including each item.

My Summer Plans

This summer, I plan to visit _____

_____

Two books I would like to read this summer

_____

_____

One new activity I would like to try this summer is

_____

My friends and I plan to _____

_____

This summer, I am going to try to _____

_____

This summer, I would really like to see _____

_____

Here is a picture of one thing I want to do this summer.

My Crystal Ball

Gazing into my crystal ball, here is how I see myself.

Next Year

In Five Years

In Ten Years

In Twenty-Five Years

Here I Am Again!

This is how I see myself at the end of the school year.

My Handwriting

This is a sample of my best handwriting. I will compare this page to my handwriting at the beginning of the school year.

Copy this paragraph:

This is a sample of my best handwriting. It is part of my own personal yearbook. Each month during this school year I added a few more pages to my book. Keeping this record helped me remember what a great year I had. It is interesting to look back through this book and see what happened this year.

What I've Learned About Myself

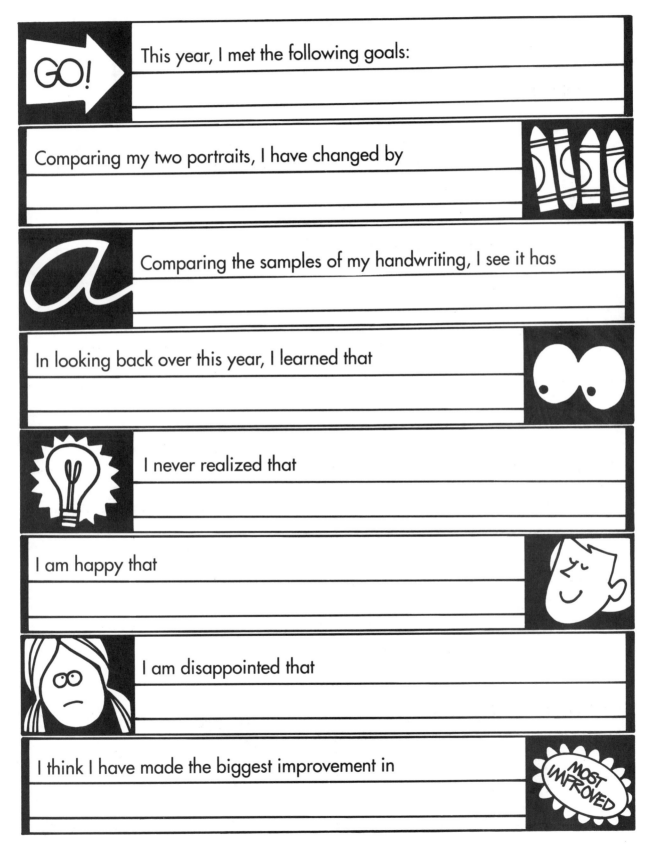

GO! This year, I met the following goals:

Comparing my two portraits, I have changed by

Comparing the samples of my handwriting, I see it has

In looking back over this year, I learned that

I never realized that

I am happy that

I am disappointed that

I think I have made the biggest improvement in

MOST IMPROVED

My Accomplishments

These are my three greatest accomplishments this year.

A Red-Letter Day

Here is a story about the very best day that I had this year.

_____

_____

_____

_____

_____

_____

_____

_____

_____

_____

_____

_____

_____

_____

_____

Memories

Here is my favorite memory from the month of

_____

_____

_____

_____

_____

_____

_____

_____

_____

_____

_____

_____

_____

_____

_____

Ideas for Pages and Projects

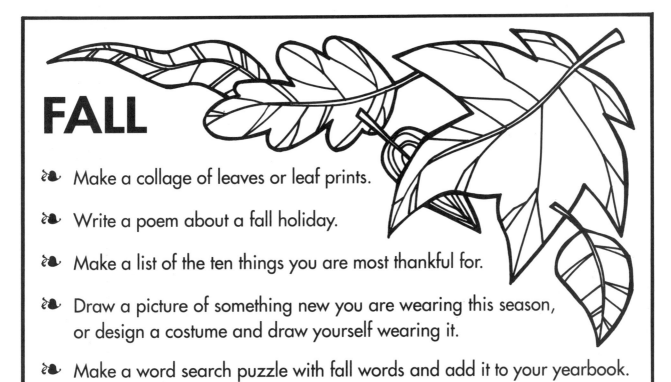

FALL

- Make a collage of leaves or leaf prints.

- Write a poem about a fall holiday.

- Make a list of the ten things you are most thankful for.

- Draw a picture of something new you are wearing this season, or design a costume and draw yourself wearing it.

- Make a word search puzzle with fall words and add it to your yearbook.

WINTER

* Write three reasons why you like this season, and three reasons why you don't like it.

* Collect winter weather stories from the newspaper and add them to your yearbook.

* Draw a picture of a gift you have received or given.

* Make a list of your family's favorite winter holiday traditions.

* Write down your New Year's resolutions.

Ideas for Pages and Projects
(continued)

SPRING

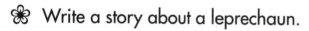
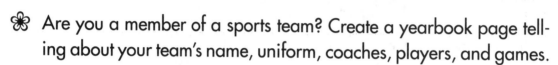

❀ Write a story about a leprechaun.

❀ Are you a member of a sports team? Create a yearbook page telling about your team's name, uniform, coaches, players, and games.

❀ Collect cartoons about spring from magazines and newspapers.

❀ Invent a new springtime holiday. Describe it in words and pictures on a yearbook page.

❀ Make a list of ideas for April Fool tricks.

❀ Design and name a new kind of butterfly.

SUMMER

✳ Add to your yearbook any letters or postcards you have received.

✳ Write about a surprising thing that happened to you this summer.

✳ Draw a picture of yourself trying to stay cool on a hot summer day.

✳ Write down the best jokes and riddles you've heard.

✳ Draw around your bare foot. Inside that shape, list things your foot did this summer.

My Story

Title:

By:

My Story

Title: _____

By: _____

_____

_____

_____

_____

_____

_____

_____

_____

_____

_____

_____

_____

_____

_____

_____

_____

_____

INK

* vacations * parties * holidays * pets *

friends * weather * movies * books * field trips * family

celebrations * sports events * contests * school activities

* games * sports * concerts * trips *

Autographs

Autographs

A Do-It-Yourself Yearbook
© The Learning Works, Inc.

Auto-graphs